THE MURDER

There are a number of people I would like to thank for helping me get this book done.

David Lloyd kept on at me to finish the novel after I showed him some sample artwork and he probably doesn't rea
quite how much that helped me. I'd also like to thank Steve Ovett for agreeing to write the foreword and for
enthusiasm for the project after seeing the initial pages.

I used quite a lot of my friends and family as models for a lot of characters in the book and in no particular order
very much like to say a big thank you to them. Tim Mayer posed for the lead character Daniel Stone and all the follow
made star appearances: Pip Adams, Liz Pichon, Harry Venning, Allan Sanders, Nishant Choksi, Tom Sanderson, Da
O'Connor, John Cole, Peter Greenwood, Charlie Collicutt, Bob Collicutt, Matt Paterson, Steve Woodgate, James Ho
Tony Holborn, Kurt Hoyte, Fred Tsjoen, Geoff Hill, Michael Merillo, Beth Bottery, Sarah Kelly, Tom Naylor, Jo
Guilmant, Charlie Grice, John Pepper, Ben Tickner, Max Pickard and Dan Stepney.

Finally I'd like to thank Emma, Doug, Lizzie and Dan, without whom this book would not have crossed the finish lir

**SELF
MADE
HERO**

First published 2013
by SelfMadeHero
5 Upper Wimpole Street
London W1G 6BP
www.selfmadehero.com

Written and Illustrated by: Paul Collicutt

Editorial Assistant: Lizzie Kaye
Publishing Director: Emma Hayley
Editor: Dan Lockwood
With thanks to: Jane Laporte, Paul Smith and Sam Humphrey

Dedication
For Clary

A CIP record for this book is available from the British Library

ISBN: 978-1-906838-62-1

10 9 8 7 6 5 4 3 2 1

Printed and bound in Slovenia

THE MURDER MILE

WRITTEN AND ILLUSTRATED BY
PAUL COLLICUTT

SELF MADE HERO

Foreword

The four-minute mile is still today a standard that runners and the general public respect as a yardstick to measure success in the sporting field of track and field athletics. Incredible then that the first time anyone successfully attempted the unthinkable of trying to run that perfect symmetry of four laps in a minute apiece was back in 1954. Others tried before, but conditions and even a World War shattered their hopes.

Athletes were desperate to become the first man to dip under the physical and psychological barrier and in doing so obtain the status of a legend. The charge took place on a worldwide stage with media following the exploits of runners from three different continents each racing time and time again against the clock, until one man in May 1954 crossed the line on a windy track in Oxford, England. Some moments later it was announced:

"Ladies and gentlemen, here is the result of event 9, the one mile: first, No. 41, R.G. Bannister, Amateur Athletic Association and formerly of Exeter and Merton Colleges, Oxford, with a time which is a new meeting and track record, and which – subject to ratification – will be a new English Native, British National, All-Comers, European, British Empire and World Record. The time was 3..." The rest of the result was drowned out by the roar of the crowd.

Steve Ovett
Olympic Gold Medallist
Two times world record holder at 1500m
Two times world mile record holder

SPRING HAD COME EARLY THIS YEAR.

HIYA, DAN. WHADDAYA RECKON... IS YOUR MAN GONNA DO IT?

I'VE GOT MONEY ON HIM, SO HE'D BETTER.

ALREADY YOU COULD FEEL THE HOT PROMISE OF SUMMER,
OF LONG DAYS AND SHORT NIGHTS, GIRLS IN BLOUSES AND COLD BEERS AT THE BEACH.
MY JOB AT THE VENNING CORPORATION WAS KEEPING ME BUSY, BUT I DIDN'T MIND.
IT WAS THE BEST FIRM OF PRIVATE INVESTIGATORS IN THE CITY, MAYBE THE BEST ANYWHERE.
I WAS LUCKY TO WORK THERE. I EVEN LIKED THE ROUTINE OF THE WALK INTO WORK.
I ALWAYS PICKED UP THE MORNING PAPER ACROSS THE STREET BEFORE I MADE
MY WAY INTO THE TAYLOR BUILDING.

EVERY DAY I GOT INTO THE ELEVATORS WITH PEOPLE WHO WORKED ON DIFFERENT FLOORS FOR DIFFERENT COMPANIES.

WHEN THE DOORS OPENED ON THE VENNING CORPORATION, I ALWAYS HAD THE FEELING THAT I'D CHOSEN THE RIGHT COMPANY TO WORK FOR.

OLD MAN VENNING RAN THE COMPANY WELL. HE WAS GOOD WITH MONEY AND GOOD WITH PEOPLE.

MORNING, DAN. HOW'S YOUR "KANSAS COWBOY" DOING?

HE'S ON GOOD FORM, PIP. ANY DAY NOW SANTEE WILL BE THE MAN.

I'D JUST FINISHED UP A BIG FRAUD INVESTIGATION AND I WONDERED WHAT CASE WOULD TAKE ME THROUGH INTO THE SUMMER MONTHS.

RUNNERS HAD BEEN HURTLING TOWARDS FOUR MINUTES SINCE THE 1930S.

AT THE BERLIN OLYMPICS, THE LAST BEFORE THE WAR, NEW ZEALAND'S JACK LOVELOCK, A MEDICAL STUDENT AT OXFORD UNIVERSITY IN ENGLAND, HAD TAKEN ON GLENN CUNNINGHAM, "THE IRON HORSE OF KANSAS" OVER THE 1500M. LOVELOCK HAD TO RUN A WORLD RECORD TO TAKE THE GOLD FROM CUNNINGHAM.

BACK IN 1933, LOVELOCK HELD THE WORLD RECORD FOR THE MILE WITH 4.07.6. CUNNINGHAM TOOK IT DOWN TO 4.06.8 THE NEXT YEAR.

"THE IRON HORSE" WAS AS TOUGH AS THEY COME. WHEN HE WAS EIGHT, HE WAS CAUGHT IN A SCHOOL FIRE THAT KILLED HIS BROTHER AND ALMOST TOOK HIS LEGS. AT FIRST THE DOCTORS WERE GOING TO AMPUTATE ONE OF THEM, BUT AFTER A NUMBER OF SKIN GRAFTS THEY SAVED IT. GLENN WAS TOLD HE'D NEVER WALK AGAIN...

...BUT HE DID! HE WORKED SO HARD THAT WITHIN A FEW YEARS HE CHALLENGED HIS SCHOOL FRIENDS TO A RACE AND BEAT THEM. THAT, HE SAID, WAS THE TOUGHEST RACE OF HIS LIFE.

4.07.6

4.06.8

4.0

BRITAIN'S SYDNEY WOODERSON, "THE MIGHTY ATOM", WAS ONLY FIVE AND HALF FEET TALL, SUFFERED FROM RHEUMATIC FEVER AND WAS PRACTICAL BLIND WITHOUT HIS SPECTACLES... BUT HE SURE COULD RUN! HE TOOK THE M DOWN TO 4.06.4 IN 1937 BUT LOST HIS BEST YEARS TO WW2. AFTER THE W HE CAME BACK AND RAN HIS QUICKEST EVER MILE IN 4.04.2 TO FINISH SECC TO ARNE ANDERSSON, ONE OF THE RUNNERS WHO HAD MOVED THE MILE RECORD CLOSER TO FOUR MINUTES.

4.02.0

4.02.0

Landy
Bannister

The Mu

velock *The Iron Horse* *The Mighty*
Anderson *of Kansas* Gunder *the Wonder*
Atom

4.01.6

4.01.4

WHILE THE REST OF THE WORLD WAS AT WAR, TWO SWEDISH ATHLETES, ANDERSSON AND GUNDER HÄGG, FOUGHT TO BE THE FIRST TO FOUR MINUTES. THEIR INTENSE RIVALRY SAW THEM BREAK THE RECORD SIX TIMES. BY 1945, "GUNDER THE WONDER" WAS THE FASTEST MILER THE WORLD HAD EVER SEEN WITH 4.01.4. THEY SURELY WOULD HAVE BROKEN THE BARRIER HAD NOT THE ATHLETIC AUTHORITIES LOOKED INTO THEIR "EXPENSES" AND BANNED THEM BOTH FOR "PROFESSIONALISM". THESE GUYS WERE FILLING STADIUMS EVERY TIME THEY RACED. YOU COULD UNDERSTAND WHY THEY MIGHT WANT PAYING!

IN 1954, "GUNDER THE WONDER" WAS STILL THE WORLD RECORD HOLDER, BUT THERE WERE MEN FROM RIGHT AROUND THE GLOBE QUEUING UP TO BREAK THAT ELUSIVE BARRIER. IN AUSTRALIA, JOHN LANDY HAD BEEN STUCK ON 4.02 FOR TWO YEARS BUT WAS LOOKING STRONGER THAN EVER. IN ARIZONA, YOUNG TODD NAYLOR, "THE PHOENIX FLYER", HAD BROKEN THROUGH TO RUN 4.03.4.

The Kansas Cowboy *The* *Phoenix Flyer*

4.02.4

4.03.4

FUNNILY ENOUGH THERE WAS ONCE AGAIN A DUEL BREWING BETWEEN A MEDICAL STUDENT FROM OXFORD UNIVERSITY AND A KANSAS STATE "JAYHAWK". ENGLAND'S ROGER BANNISTER WAS ON 4.02.0 AND WES SANTEE, "THE KANSAS COWBOY", WAS RUNNING HIM DOWN WITH 4.02.4. EVERY DAY I READ THE PAPERS, WAITING FOR THE MOMENT WHEN SANTEE WOULD BREAK THAT BARRIER AND MAKE THE MILE AMERICA'S.

THEN, IN AN INSTANT, MY WHOLE OUTLOOK CHANGED...

der Mile

DAN, THE OLD MAN WANTS TO SEE YOU IN HIS OFFICE RIGHT NOW, SO YOU'D BETTER HAUL YOUR ASS DOWN THERE.

ALRIGHT, PIP, I'M HAULING.

MORNING, DAN. THIS IS DEAN CAULDWELL. HE NEEDS OUR HELP AND I BELIEVE THAT YOU JUST MIGHT BE THE RIGHT MAN FOR THIS JOB.

HAVE YOU HEARD OF AN ATHLETE CALLED TODD NAYLOR?

SURE... HE'S THE "PHOENIX FLYER".

HE RUNS THE MILE AND LOOKS SET TO CHASE WES SANTEE TO FOUR MINUTES. HE'S ONE OF OUR BRIGHTEST YOUNG TALENTS.

WELL, TWO DAYS AGO TODD NAYLOR WAS FOUND DEAD, FACE DOWN IN THE DESERT.

JUST LIKE THAT "THE PHOENIX FLYER" HAD COME TO A STOP. NOW SANTEE WAS ON HIS OWN AGAINST THE REST OF THE WORLD.

THE LOCAL POLICE WERE AS HELPFUL AS THEY COULD BE. THE VENNING CORPORATION HAD A GOOD REPUTATION FOR WORKING WITH THE AUTHORITIES AND NOT BEHIND THEIR BACKS.

THESE ARE THE CRIME SCENE PHOTOGRAPHS.

NAYLOR WAS FOUND FACE DOWN IN THE DESERT SAND. IT LOOKED LIKE HE'D FALLEN FROM A TRAIL UP THE SIDE OF THIS HILL.

HIS HEAD WAS CUT FROM IMPACT WITH THIS BOULDER. AS YOU CAN SEE IT'S NOT SOMETHING THAT COULD BE THROWN.

SO, INSPECTOR SCOTT, DID HE FALL OR WAS HE PUSHED?

AT FIRST WE THOUGHT HE'D FALLEN. THERE ARE NO FOOTPRINTS IN THE SAND TO SUGGEST THAT ANYONE ELSE WAS THERE. BUT WHAT MADE US SUSPICIOUS IS THAT THERE AREN'T ANY FOOTPRINTS, PERIOD.

WHAT WAS HE DOING OUT THERE ANYWAY?

RUNNING. APPARENTLY HE OFTEN DROVE OUT TO THE DESERT AND RAN OVER THE TRAILS.

WAS HIS CAR STILL THERE?

YES... AND INTERESTINGLY THERE WERE NO TYRE TRACKS AT ALL.

I BELIEVE YOU FOUND SOME ITEMS IN NAYLOR'S CAR.

THAT'S RIGHT... IN AN ENVELOPE WHICH HAD A UNIVERSITY ATHLETIC DEPARTMENT LOGO ON IT, WE FOUND $1,000. AND A LIST OF BIG MILE RACES COMING UP. SOME OF THEM ARE MARKED AND NEXT TO THEM ARE WRITTEN WHAT WE SUPPOSE TO BE PLACINGS, LIKE 3RD OR 2ND...

SOME OF THESE RACES HAVE HAPPENED ALREADY AND TODD NAYLOR FINISHED IN THOSE POSITIONS. SOME ARE STILL TO COME.

ON THE BACK OF THE ENVELOPE IS COACH JOHN CARLTON'S NAME, WRITTEN IN PENCIL BUT NOT IN ANY HANDWRITING WE CAN IDENTIFY... ALSO WRITTEN NEXT TO CARLTON'S NAME IS "$20,000".

HAVE YOU MADE ANY PROGRESS?

NONE WHATSOEVER.

THE CHIEF SUDDENLY REALLOCATED OUR DETECTIVES. THERE'S A BIG FRAUD AND MURDER CASE TAKING UP ALL OUR PERSONNEL, SO THIS IS ON THE BACK BURNER FOR A WHILE...

DOESN'T NORMALLY HAPPEN, BUT I GUESS THERE'S A LOT OF PEOPLE ON VACATION RIGHT NOW.

TO BE HONEST, YOUR INVOLVEMENT TAKES SOME OF THE PRESSURE OFF US. YOU CAN READ ALL THE FILES AS LONG AS YOU REPORT BACK TO US WITH ANY NEW INFORMATION YOU GET.

NEXT STOP WAS THE UNIVERSITY ATHLETIC DEPT. AND A FACE FROM MY PAST.

COACH CARLTON WAS TRACKSIDE TIMING A SESSION. I SAT IN THE STANDS AND WAITED FOR HIM TO FINISH.

LAST REPETITION, GUYS. KEEP IT TOGETHER... NO LAST LAP HEROES... YOU'VE ALL GOT THE KANSAS RELAYS IN TWO DAYS.

THE RUNNERS SET OFF ON ONE MORE LAP AROUND THE TRACK. WORKING AS ONE MACHINE, THEY FORCED THEMSELVES THROUGH TO THE END OF THE SESSION AS THE COACH BARKED OUT THEIR TIMES. IT ALL SEEMED SO FAMILIAR.

IT FELT LIKE YESTERDAY.

APRIL 1944. DITCHLING COMMON CRICKET GROUND, SUSSEX, ENGLAND. INTER-SERVICES SPORTS MATCH.

I'D BEEN IN TRAINING BACK THEN. NOT ESPECIALLY FOR TRACK RUNNING, MORE FOR INVADING ANOTHER COUNTRY. BUT SO HAD ALL MY FELLOW COMPETITORS THAT DAY.

THE INTER-SERVICES SPORTS MATCH WAS A WELCOME RELIEF FROM SOLDIERING.

ALRIGHT, LIEUTENANT, THEY'RE CALLING FOR THE MILE.

THANKS, SARGE. I FEEL GOOD TODAY. I THINK I'M GONNA WIN.

WATCH OUT FOR THAT LITTLE BRIT.

WHAT, THAT GUY IN THE GLASSES?

17

I REMEMBER THAT RACE VIVIDLY. THE GRASS WAS SO WELL ROLLED IT FELT LIKE WE WERE RUNNING ON CARPET.

THE LITTLE GUY HUNG BACK AND I PUT HIM OUT OF MY MIND.

HEY, THE LIEUTENANT LOOKS GOOD IN SECOND PLACE. SARGE, WE'RE ALL GONNA WIN ON THIS!

YEAH, SURE. JUST WAIT A WHILE.

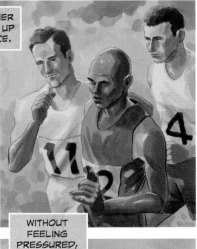

I LET THE OTHER RUNNERS TAKE UP THE EARLY PACE.

WITHOUT FEELING PRESSURED, I MOVED TO THE FRONT.

I COULD FEEL THE OTHERS CLOSING ME DOWN BUT I HELD ON FOR SECOND.

AS WE CLOSED IN ON THE FINISH, THE CROWDS ALMOST JOINED US ON THE GRASS TRACK.

GOOD RACE, MATE. I ENJOYED THAT.

THANKS, BUDDY. YOU'VE GOT SOME MAGIC IN THOSE LEGS.

DAMN, SARGE! WE'VE LOST OUR MONEY!

NO, YOU HAVEN'T, BOYS. I PUT IT ALL ON THE BRIT FOR YOU.

THAT, BOYS, IS SYDNEY WOODERSON, "THE MIGHTY ATOM", AND BEFORE THIS OLD WAR STARTED HE WAS THE WORLD RECORD HOLDER FOR THE MILE.

WHY ARE THE MEN SO HAPPY?

THEY'VE ALL JUST BEEN CONVERTED TO TRACK AND FIELD!

21

GOOD SESSION. WARM DOWN, THEN HIT THE SHOWERS... AND STAY OFF THE BOOZE UNTIL AFTER THE MEET... THEN YOU CAN PARTY.

OK, COACH.

YEAH... FOR JOHN CARLTON - WHO I HADN'T SEEN SINCE WE DEMOBBED AT THE END OF THE WAR - TRACK AND FIELD WAS ALMOST A RELIGION.

SERGEANT CARLTON!

LOOKING GOOD, SARGE.

HELL! CAPTAIN STONE!

STILL RUNNING, CAPTAIN? YOU LOOK LIKE YOU KEEP IN SHAPE.

I DO A LITTLE BIT WHEN I CAN, SARGE. WHEN WE ALL GOT BACK AFTER THE WAR I JUST DIDN'T FEEL LIKE IT FOR A WHILE, BUT NOW I KIND OF ENJOY IT WHEN I'VE GOT THE TIME.

I'M GOING TO HAVE TO GET A LOOK AT ALL YOUR RECORDS SOMETIME, JOHN. AND I'LL PROBABLY HAVE TO TALK TO SOME OF YOUR ATHLETES.

GO WHERE YOU WANT AND TALK TO ANYONE YOU LIKE. YOU MIGHT WANT TO START WITH HIS GIRLFRIEND OR HIS ROOMMATE.

THANKS, SARGE.

THE JANITOR LET ME INTO TODD'S ROOM AND I WAS LOOKING THROUGH BOXES OF HIS BELONGINGS WHEN HIS ROOMMATE CAME IN.

HI. YOU MUST BE DANIEL STONE. THE DEAN TOLD ME ABOUT YOU. SAID WE HAD TO HELP YOU.

WHAT WAS TODD LIKE?

PRETTY GOOD GUY. EASY TO SHARE A ROOM WITH. HE LOVED HIS RUNNING, NEVER MISSED A DAY'S TRAINING.

HE WAS QUITE METHODICAL. ALWAYS RECORDED EVERYTHING IN HIS TRAINING DIARY.

HIS TRAINING DIARY! WHERE'D HE KEEP IT?

HERE... IN THE DRAWER OF HIS DESK. BUT IT'S NOT THERE ANY MORE.

I KNOW BECAUSE I LOOKED FOR IT WHEN THOSE TWO POLICE DETECTIVES CAME ROUND...

THEY WERE KEEN TO SEE IT AS WELL.

NEXT UP WAS HIS GIRLFRIEND JACQUELINE, A HISTORY OF ART STUDENT. SHE WAS STILL PRETTY UPSET ABOUT THE WHOLE THING.

PEOPLE ARE SAYING TODD AND COACH CARLTON WERE THROWING RACES. I DON'T BELIEVE TODD WOULD HAVE DONE THAT.

WHAT ABOUT COACH?

I DON'T REALLY KNOW. THERE WAS SOMETHING GOING ON BECAUSE TWO POLICEMEN CAME ROUND TO TALK TO TODD ABOUT COACH.

I DON'T KNOW WHAT THEY SAID BUT TODD GOT REAL ANGRY ABOUT SOMETHING AND WENT OFF TO SEE COACH.

TODD WOULDN'T SAY WHAT WAS GOING ON. I KNOW HE WAS VERY LOYAL TO COACH AND WOULDN'T TELL TALES ON HIM. THE NEXT WEEK, TODD DROVE OUT TO THE DESERT FOR A RUN AND NEVER CAME BACK.

HE LAY OUT THERE OVERNIGHT UNTIL SOMEONE FOUND HIM THE NEXT DAY.

DID THE POLICEMEN EVER COME BACK?

YES. THEY WERE THE ONES WHO CAME TO ASK ABOUT TODD'S DEATH. SOME PEOPLE ARE SAYING IT WAS MURDER... DO YOU KNOW?

NO, I'M AFRAID I DON'T. BUT TELL ME WHAT THE POLICEMEN WANTED TO KNOW.

JUST GENERAL BACKGROUND INFORMATION, BUT THEY ALSO ASKED HOW HE GOT ON WITH COACH AND IF HE'D SAID ANYTHING ABOUT COACH CARLTON RECENTLY.

OH YES, AND THEY WANTED TO KNOW IF HE HAD A DIARY OF HIS TRAINING AND RACES.

I TOLD THEM SURE HE HAD, HE KEPT IT IN HIS ROOM. HE WROTE EVERYTHING IN IT... WHEN WE FIRST MET, EVERY DATE WE EVER WENT ON.

EVERYTHING THAT WAS IMPORTANT TO TODD HE WROTE DOWN IN THAT BOOK. HE WANTED TO BE A JOURNALIST AFTER UNIVERSITY.

HAVE YOU EVER SEEN THESE POLICEMEN AGAIN, JACQUELINE?

NOT TO TALK TO, BUT I HAVE SEEN THEM WALKING AROUND THE GROUNDS ONCE OR TWICE.

SOMETHING DIDN'T ADD UP. ACCORDING TO INSPECTOR SCOTT, ALL THE DETECTIVES HAD BEEN REASSIGNED. SO WHAT WERE THEY DOING SNIFFING ABOUT DOWN HERE?

COACH CARLTON TOOK HIS TEAM TO THE KANSAS RELAYS, AND WHILE WE ENJOYED BRIGHT SPRING DAYS THEY ENDURED RAIN AND HAIL.

Kansas Relays
Saturday April 17 1954

BILL EASTON, THE KANSAS UNIVERSITY HEAD COACH, WAS A WORRIED MAN.

FOR YEARS, SANTEE HAD SERVED THE UNIVERSITY TEAM SELFLESSLY, RUNNING MULTIPLE EVENTS AT EVERY MEETING AND PUTTING TEAM POINTS AHEAD OF THE FOUR-MINUTE MILE.

TODAY EASTON HAD PROMISED HIM PAYBACK.

BUT WHEN EASTON WOKE UP THAT MORNING, HE KNEW THAT FATE HAD CONSPIRED AGAINST SANTEE.

THE TRACK WAS AWASH, THE CINDERS HEAVY WITH WATER, WHEN "THE KANSAS COWBOY" STEPPED ONTO IT.

SANTEE'S TEAM MATES SPRANG INTO ACTION MOPPING UP THE WATER, WHILE WES SANTEE PROWLED AROUND THE KANSAS STADIUM, PREPARING HIMSELF FOR THE HERCULEAN TASK AHEAD.

29

AS SOON AS THE RACE STARTED, SANTEE COULD FEEL THE TRACK FIGHTING AGAINST HIM.

HE SET OFF WITH PURPOSE. THIS WAS MEANT TO BE HIS DAY.

HE KNEW THAT THE FIRST FOUR-MINUTE MILE WAS IN HIS LEGS.

COACH EASTON HAD TRIED EVERYTHING TO DRY OUT THE TRACK. HE'D EVEN POURED OIL ON THE CINDERS AND SET FIRE TO IT HOPING IN VAIN THAT IT WOULD BURN OFF THE MOISTURE.

NOW THERE WAS NOTHING MORE HE COULD DO TO HELP HIS ATHLETE.

SANTEE ROLLED ON AND ON, PLOUGHING A FURROW ON THE INSIDE LANE OF THE TRACK.

HIS BODY WAS CRYING OUT TO STOP BUT HE COULDN'T LET DOWN HIS TEAM, HIS COACH, HIS UNIVERSITY AND ALL THE CROWDS WHO HAD STAYED ON THROUGH THE THUNDER AND HAILSTORMS TO CHEER HIM ALONG.

WITH EVERY STRIDE, SANTEE SANK DEEPER INTO THE TRACK.

BUT STILL HE PUSHED ON.

BY THE LAST LAP IT WAS LIKE RUNNING ACROSS A MUDDY FIELD.

WITHOUT ANY PACEMAKERS HE FOUGHT HIS WAY ROUND THE MILE TO 4.03.1. THE WEATHER HAD CONSPIRED AGAINST SANTEE BUT IT WAS SURELY ONLY A MATTER OF TIME.

JOHN LANDY HAD FINISHED HIS TRACK SEASON IN AUSTRALIA AND WAS PREPARING TO RUN IN EUROPE, AND BANNISTER WAS GEARING UP FOR HIS TRACK SEASON.

BUT FOR MY MONEY WES SANTEE WOULD GET THERE FIRST. HE SHOULD HAVE ALREADY DONE IT IN KANSAS... BUT WHO'D HEARD OF HAILSTORMS AT A TRACK MEET?

4.03.1

COACH EASTON AND WES SANTEE BOTH KNEW THIS DAY SHOULD HAVE BEEN THEIRS.

THE FANS KNEW IT TOO, BUT THEY ALSO KNEW HE'D GIVEN IT EVERYTHING HE HAD.

BEFORE COACH CARLTON GOT BACK, I WANTED TO MAKE A START ON GOING THROUGH HIS RECORDS. HE'D LEFT SOME KEYS FOR ME TO GET INTO THE ATHLETIC DEPARTMENT OFFICES.

I FELT A BIT ODD RIFLING THROUGH HIS PAPERS, BUT I HAD A JOB TO DO AND THE REPUTATION OF THE VENNING CORPORATION TO UPHOLD... ALWAYS GOOD TO REMEMBER WHO PAYS YOUR WAGES!

I FOUND ALL THE FILES HE HAD ON HIS ATHLETES AND PULLED OUT TODD NAYLOR'S DETAILS.

HE WAS IN THE MIDDLE OF A THREE-YEAR COURSE AND WAS A PRETTY VALUABLE ASSET TO THE UNIVERSITY, BEING ONE OF THEIR BIGGEST POINTS SCORERS AT TRACK MEETS.

I WAS STUDYING THE DETAILS OF HIS RACING SCHEDULE AND NOT PAYING ANY ATTENTION TO MUCH ELSE.

YOU'D THINK THAT BY NOW I'D REMEMBER TO WATCH MY BACK EVERY TIME.

GET AWAY FROM THOSE PAPERS! NOW!

BEFORE I HAD A CHANCE TO GET A WORD OUT THIS BIG GUY HAD RUSHED AT ME.

HE'D STOPPED TALKING AND NOW I WAS OFF BALANCE. WHO WAS THIS APE?

33

THIS GUY WAS QUICK. QUICK LIKE A SPRINTER! THAT SUITED ME FINE.

I KNEW I WASN'T IN THE SHAPE I WAS TEN YEARS AGO, BUT I STILL COULD RUN.

YOU SEE, A SPRINTER WILL FLY OUT OF THE BLOCKS BUT THE LONGER THEY RUN FOR THE SLOWER THEY GET.

ME... I KNEW I COULD KEEP GOING A BIT LONGER.

I WAS CLOSING FAST.

WHAT WAS IN THAT LITTLE RED BOOK?

WHAT WAS SO IMPORTANT? AND WHY WAS IT IN CARLTON'S OFFICE?

I MIGHT BE CLOSING ON HIM, BUT MY LUNGS WERE STARTING TO BURN.

WHO WAS THIS GUY AND MORE IMPORTANTLY WHEN WOULD HE STOP?

THAT'S JUST ABOUT WHEN I FIRST FELL FOR ALISON...

I'M DANIEL STONE, A PRIVATE INVESTIGATOR BROUGHT IN BY THE UNIVERSITY TO INVESTIGATE THE DEATH OF TODD NAYLOR.

BUT WHO ON EARTH WERE YOU CHASING AFTER LIKE THAT?

I HAVE ABSOLUTELY NO IDEA. ALL I KNOW IS THAT HE'S STOLEN TODD NAYLOR'S TRAINING DIARY, WHICH MAY HAVE HAD VALUABLE INFORMATION IN IT.

YOU KNOW, YOU STILL HAVEN'T TOLD ME YOUR NAME.

I'M ALISON. ALISON RENDALL.

I USED TO SEE TODD NAYLOR AROUND HERE ALL THE TIME. I WORK IN THE ADMINISTRATION BUILDING AND HE WAS ALWAYS POPPING BY... IN FACT, HE WAS IN LAST WEEK.

REALLY. WHAT FOR?

YOU KNOW, I THINK HE WAS SORTING OUT SOMETHING ABOUT ONE OF HIS COURSES. BUT...

WELL, IT'S JUST A THOUGHT BUT I'M SURE HE DECIDED TO DO SOMETHING ELSE WHILE HE WAS THERE.

LET ME GIVE YOU MY CARD.

MY NUMBER'S ON THERE. IF YOU THINK OF ANYTHING ELSE...

...CALL ME. DAY OR NIGHT.

YOU KNOW, I JUST MIGHT.

THE NEXT FEW DAYS WERE OFFICE-BASED, SORTING THROUGH PAPERS FROM COACH CARLTON'S OFFICE.

DAN, I'VE BEEN LOOKING INTO BETTING ON MILE RACES LIKE YOU ASKED ME TO. THERE HAVE BEEN SOME BIG PAYOUTS RECENTLY ON COLLEGE RACES. IT SEEMS THEY WERE SPREAD BETWEEN FOUR BOOKIES. THE BIG BETS WERE NEVER PLACED TWICE AT THE SAME PLACE.

EXCELLENT. YOU'RE DOING BETTER THAN I AM, PIP. SO FAR I CAN FIND NOTHING THAT WOULD LINK CARLTON OR NAYLOR TO BETTING.

ANY NEWS ON THE GUY WHO KNOCKED YOU DOWN OR THOSE TWO POLICE OFFICERS?

NO. INSPECTOR SCOTT CONFIRMED THAT THEY HADN'T SENT ANY OFFICERS TO THE UNIVERSITY AND NO ONE HAS SEEN THE BIG GUY AGAIN.

BRING! BRING!

PHONE FOR YOU, DAN.

OH, HI. THIS IS A PLEASANT SURPRISE.

I'VE GOT THE AFTERNOON OFF AND I'M GOING TO BE AT CAP'S DINER FROM ONE O'CLOCK. I'VE GOT SOME INFORMATION FOR YOU ABOUT TODD NAYLOR... IF YOU'RE INTERESTED.

"I'LL BE THERE."

PIP, I'M OUT OF THE OFFICE THIS AFTERNOON IF ANYONE CALLS FOR ME.

AS I DROVE OUT TOWARDS CAP'S I PONDERED ON THE SLOWNESS OF THIS CASE. I NEEDED SOME MORE INFORMATION BEFORE I COULD GO BACK TO COACH JOHN CARLTON.

THE POLICE WERE STILL NOT CALLING NAYLOR'S DEATH MURDER BUT THEY HAD LEFT A LOT UP IN THE AIR.

I WAS CERTAIN THIS WAS ALL TIED UP WITH BETTING ON RACES. JOHN CARLTON HAD NEVER BEEN AVERSE TO A BET. WAS HE INVOLVED?

BUT IT WASN'T JUST THE PROMISE OF INFORMATION THAT HAD ME DRIVING OUT TO THIS MEETING.

I HOPED NOT BUT I HAD TO BE SURE.

CAP'S WAS A POPULAR OUT-OF-TOWN DINER THAT HAD SPRUNG UP IN THE LAST FEW YEARS. THEY WERE BUILDING EVERYWHERE THESE DAYS.

ON A BRIGHT MAY DAY LIKE THIS, I WAS HAPPY TO BE OUT OF THE CITY FOR A WHILE.

YOU NEVER KNOW WHAT A MEETING LIKE THIS MIGHT LEAD TO, BUT IT'S ALWAYS BEST TO BE PREPARED.

I WAS INTRIGUED BY WHAT ALISON HAD TO SAY. I WAS INTRIGUED BY HER.

THEN YESTERDAY I REMEMBERED. HE HAD A BOOK FOR COACH CARLTON.

HE LEFT IT IN COACH'S PIGEON HOLE.

THEN THAT MUST HAVE BEEN HIS TRAINING DIARY. THE ONE THAT STRANGER STOLE.

WELL, THIS ISN'T THE BOOK THAT GOT STOLEN. COACH HARDLY EVER COLLECTS HIS MAIL, SO IT WAS LYING IN HIS PIGEON HOLE AFTER THAT DAY WE MET.

DID ANYONE ELSE HAVE AN OPPORTUNITY TO SEE THIS SECOND BOOK?

I DON'T THINK ANYONE KNEW IT WAS THERE. I SPOKE TO COACH, AND HE TOLD ME TO TRUST YOU.

ALRIGHT, IS THE BOOK STILL THERE?

I BROUGHT IT WITH ME. I KNEW YOU'D WANT TO SEE IT RIGHT AWAY.

WELL, YOU ARE FULL OF SURPRISES.

...AND IT WAS A GOOD EXCUSE TO CALL YOU AS WELL.

WAIT, THIS IS NAYLOR'S DIARY! IF THIS BOOK REVEALS ANYTHING THEN I RECKON I'LL OWE YOU DINNER IN TOWN.

THAT WOULD BE... VERY NICE INDEED.

HA. WHAT A STROKE OF LUCK THAT NAYLOR WAS STUDYING JOURNALISM. HE JUST COULDN'T STOP WRITING EVERYTHING DOWN.

WHAT DOES HE SAY ABOUT THOSE POLICEMEN?

LET'S SEE... "TWO OUT-OF-TOWN POLICE OFFICERS CAME TO SEE ME TODAY."

"THEY WEREN'T HERE ON POLICE BUSINESS, THEY WANTED ME TO THROW RACES... OFFERED ABOUT $1,000 PER BIG RACE IF I DID WHAT THEY SAID."

43

44

THAT EVENING, I WANTED TO CHECK OUT THE BETTING ANGLE THAT PIP HAD LOOKED INTO, WHICH IS HOW I FOUND MYSELF IN O'CONNOR'S BAR ON A WEDNESDAY NIGHT WITH MY BOOKIE!

EVERYBODY'S INTERESTED IN THIS FOUR-MINUTE MILE RIGHT NOW, DAN. ALL THE BOOKIES ACROSS TOWN ARE TAKING BETS.

ANY UNUSUAL ONES, DAVE?

47

THE NEXT DAY, I TOOK LUNCH BY MYSELF. IT GAVE ME TIME TO THINK ABOUT THE CASE AND TO READ THE MORNING SPORTS PAGES. "THE KANSAS COWBOY" WAS STILL CONFIDENT IN HIS ABILITIES.

ON THE STREET, THE LATEST SPORTS HEADLINES STOPPED ME DEAD.

LATEST! LIMEY ROGER BANNISTER RUNS FOUR-MINUTE MILE.

DAMN! HE'D DONE IT!

THREE MINUTES AND 59.4 SECONDS.

IT LOOKED LIKE EVERYONE WAS INTERESTED IN THIS STORY.

ONLY A FEW HOURS LATER DID I REALIZE THAT I WOULDN'T BE COLLECTING ON THAT $100 BET WITH DAVE.

OF COURSE, IT ALSO MEANT THAT THE MYSTERY MAN WOULDN'T BE COLLECTING ON ANY OF HIS $20,000 BETS EITHER.

I MIGHT NOT HAVE THE CHANCE TO TRACK DOWN THIS STRANGER SOON, BUT TONIGHT THERE WOULD BE FOUR BOOKIES OUT THERE WHO WOULD BE VERY HAPPY.

MEANWHILE I HAD AN AFTERNOON DATE WITH ALISON.

THE FEATURE'S NOT DUE TO START FOR A WHILE, BUT WE'D BETTER GET IN IF YOU WANT TO CATCH THE NEWSREEL.

I KNOW WHAT YOU'RE KEEN TO SEE!

THAT OBVIOUS HUH?

TRUE, THE NEWSREEL FROM ENGLAND WAS WHAT I WANTED TO SEE.

THURSDAY 6TH MAY 1954, IFFLEY ROAD RUNNING TRACK, OXFORD, ENGLAND.

ACROSS THE ATLANTIC, BANNISTER HAD TAKEN HIS CHANCE FOR GLORY.

BANNISTER KNEW THAT SANTEE WOULD HAVE ANOTHER SHOT AT THE MILE SOON AND THAT LANDY WAS PREPARING FOR THE EUROPEAN SEASON, SO HE HAD HAD TO GET IN HIS EFFORT QUICKLY.

"BANNISTER BREAKS THE FOUR-MINUTE MILE. THE MOST SOUGHT-AFTER TARGET IN ATHLETICS..."

THAT DAY, JOHN LANDY WAS SITTING IN A RESTAURANT IN FINLAND AND WES SANTEE WAS TRAINING WITH HIS COACH AT THE UNIVERSITY OF KANSAS.

UNLIKE SANTEE AND LANDY, BANNISTER WAS GOING TO USE PACEMAKERS... TWO OF THEM.

IT WAS A MATCH BETWEEN OXFORD UNIVERSITY AND THE ENGLISH AMATEUR ATHLETIC ASSOCIATION. BANNISTER AND HIS TWO FRIENDS WERE RUNNING FOR THE AAA.

"FEWER THAN 3,000 PEOPLE, MOSTLY UNDERGRADUATES, WERE THERE TO SEE ROGER BANNISTER..."

STEADILY, STOICALLY, THE THREE RUNNERS SWEPT AROUND THE TRACK IN OXFORD.

IT WAS A LITTLE BIT CLOUDY AND BLUSTERY, BUT NOTHING LIKE THE HAILSTORMS AND WATER-LOGGED TRACK SANTEE HAD COME UP AGAINST IN KANSAS.

CHRIS BRASHER, THE FIRST PACEMAKER, MOVED ASIDE AND CHRISTOPHER CHATAWAY TOOK UP THE DUTIES.

BANNISTER MOVED LIKE A MAN ABOUT TO MAKE HISTORY.

THE UNFOLDING DRAMA WAS MESMERIZING.

BANNISTER STAYED CLOSE IN BEHIND HIS LAST PACEMAKER UNTIL HALFWAY ROUND THE VERY LAST LAP.

THEN HE PULLED AWAY, MAJESTICALLY, IMPERIOUSLY STRIDING ACROSS THE CINDERS.

BANNISTER CHARGED TOWARDS THE LINE. THIS WAS IT, THE MOMENT OF TRUTH.

EVEN KNOWING THE RESULT, I FOUND MYSELF HOLDING MY BREATH.

"THE TAPE IS BROKEN AND SO IS THE RECORD ATHLETES HAVE LONG BEEN DREAMING ABOUT..."

IT WAS DONE AND NOBODY ELSE WOULD EVER BE THE FIRST AGAIN.

3:59.4

WHAT MUST IT FEEL LIKE TO BE ROGER BANNISTER?

WHAT MUST IT FEEL LIKE TO BE JOHN LANDY OR WES SANTEE?

ONCE AGAIN THE WORLD HAD MOVED ON.

SO THERE IT WAS IN BLACK AND WHITE, FLICKERING ACROSS A SCREEN... THE MILE IN UNDER FOUR MINUTES.

OUTSIDE IT WAS STILL A SUNNY AFTERNOON. PEOPLE BREAK BARRIERS AND THE WORLD STILL GOES ABOUT ITS OWN BUSINESS.

HOW MANY OF THESE PEOPLE COULD RUN THAT FAST? WAS THIS FOR ONLY THE MOST ELITE ATHLETES OR WOULD IT ONE DAY BECOME COMMONPLACE?

GOT ANY PLANS FOR THE REST OF THE DAY, DAN?

NO. I'VE JUST GOT TO CALL BY THE OFFICE AND PICK UP SOME MESSAGES AND THEN I'M YOURS FOR THE WEEKEND.

GOOD. MAYBE WE CAN FIND SOMETHING TO DO THAT TAKES LONGER THAN FOUR MINUTES.

ALL THOUGHTS OF ATHLETES RACING AROUND TRACKS VANISHED FROM MY MIND.

HAH. WELL, LET'S START WITH A NICE SLOW WALK TO MY OFFICE.

55

WE WALKED THROUGH THE CITY, SOAKING UP THE WARM SPRING SUNSHINE. WE WALKED WITHOUT ANY HASTE.

IT WAS NICE FOR A WHILE TO LET OTHERS CONCERN THEMSELVES WITH TIME, TO SQUANDER THE PRECIOUS COMMODITY THAT PEOPLE LIKE BANNISTER SO OBSESSED ABOUT.

DO YOU THINK TODD COULD HAVE BEATEN BANNISTER TO THE FOUR-MINUTE MILE?

HE WAS PROBABLY TOO YOUNG TO DO IT RIGHT NOW. BUT I THINK HE WOULD HAVE DONE IT EVENTUALLY.

I GUESS WE'LL NEVER KNOW.

SO WHAT ABOUT THOSE WEEKEND PLANS? WE COULD TAKE A TRIP OUT OF THE CITY.

BEFORE WE COULD GET TOO FAR INTO OUR PLANS, WE WERE INTERRUPTED BY A SHOUT...

STONE! DANIEL STONE!

AGENT STEPHEN ASHENFELTER. FBI. MAY I HAVE A WORD WITH YOU ABOUT THE TODD NAYLOR MURDER?

MURDER! SO IT'S BEEN CALLED FOR SURE?

WE'RE CALLING IT. TELL ME, DID IT STRIKE YOU AS STRANGE THAT ALL THE OFFICERS INVESTIGATING NAYLOR'S DEATH WERE SUDDENLY REASSIGNED?

WELL, WE NEED YOUR HELP. SOMEONE HAS JUST THREATENED TO KILL WES SANTEE AND A NUMBER OF OTHER ATHLETES, AND WE BELIEVE THE CULPRIT IS ON THE POLICE FORCE!

OF COURSE IT DID. IT MADE ME THINK THERE WAS SOMETHING ELSE GOING ON AS WELL.

WHAT?!

WE THINK THE SAME MANIAC WHO SENT THESE DEATH THREATS WAS ALSO INVOLVED IN TODD NAYLOR'S MURDER, AS WELL AS TODAY'S SHOOTING OF COACH JOHN CARLTON!

GOOD GRIEF!

RUN! MOVE THE LEAD! GO!

A GOOD RACE IS ALL ABOUT PACING. IT'S AS MUCH ABOUT HOLDING YOURSELF BACK AS IT IS ABOUT FORGING FORWARD. YOU NEED TO KEEP A COOL HEAD AT ALL TIMES. TRY TO MAKE SURE YOU HAVE GOOD SIGHT OF THE FRONT OF THE RACE. TRY NOT TO GET BOXED IN BY THE OTHER RUNNERS.

THE THIRD QUARTER IS ALWAYS THE MOST DIFFICULT. YOU MUST TRY TO RETAIN YOUR RESOLUTION.

ON THE LAST LAP, GATHER YOUR STRENGTH FOR THE FINAL SPRINT. YOU MUST MAKE SURE NOT TO GO TOO EARLY AND OVERREACH YOURSELF. NOR MUST YOU LEAVE IT TOO LATE AND UNDERACHIEVE.

THE LAST EFFORT WILL REQUIRE ALL YOUR STRENGTH AND MAY HURT BUT YOU MUST PUSH ON THROUGH TO THE TAPE.

HEY, CAPTAIN! DID YOU BRING ANY FLOWERS?

SORRY, I DIDN'T HAVE TIME. I KNEW THEY COULDN'T KILL YOU WITH BULLETS, JOHN, BUT WHEN I HEARD YOU WERE IN A HOSPITAL BED I GOT WORRIED, SO I HIGHTAILED IT OVER HERE AS FAST AS I COULD.

ALL HEART!

WHO DID THIS, JOHN?

NO IDEA, CAPTAIN. I WAS WALKING ACROSS THE UNIVERSITY CAMPUS, HEARD A SHOT AND THE NEXT THING I KNEW I WAS LYING ON THE GROUND.

WHOEVER IT WAS ONLY GOT ME IN THE SHOULDER AND THEY DIDN'T TRY FOR ANOTHER SHOT. I HEARD SCREAMS, THE SOUND OF PEOPLE RUNNING AND THEN I WOKE UP IN HOSPITAL.

JOHN, I NEED TO ASK YOU SOME QUESTIONS ARE YOU UP TO IT?

YEAH. WE'VE BOTH HAD WORSE, RIGHT?

TODD NAYLOR CAME TO SEE YOU BEFORE HE DIED. WHAT DID HE SAY?

IT WAS KIND OF STRANGE. HE STARTED TALKING ABOUT BETTING ON RACES. HE WAS TALKING AROUND THE SUBJECT THOUGH... LIKE HE HAD SOMETHING TO SAY BUT DIDN'T WANT TO SAY IT.

WE TALKED ABOUT HOW DIFFICULT IT WOULD BE TO REALLY THROW A RACE... HOW UNCERTAIN.

DID HE ASK YOU DIRECTLY ABOUT BETTING?

I THINK HE ASKED ME IF I'D EVER BET ON A RACE. I SAID I HAD IN THE PAST BUT IN MY POSITION AS CHIEF COACH I COULDN'T ANY MORE.

AND I ADDED THAT IF I EVER FOUND AN ATHLETE OF MINE THROWING RACES THEY'D BE KICKED OFF THE TEAM... QUICK SHARP.

DID HE MENTION ANY POLICEMEN OR ANYTHING ELSE?

NOPE. LOOK, CAPTAIN, I JUST DON'T BELIEVE TODD WAS THE SORT OF KID WHO WOULD THROW RACES.

JOHN, WHEN I WAS IN YOUR OFFICE A BOOK WAS STOLEN BY SOME GOON. I THOUGHT IT WAS TODD'S TRAINING DIARY; BUT THAT TURNED UP LATER, SO... WHAT WAS IT?

THERE WAS ONLY ONE BOOK MISSING, CAPTAIN - MY OWN PRIVATE NOTEBOOK, FILLED WITH MY NOTES ON ATHLETES' FORM, THEIR SCHEDULES AND RESULTS, AND MY PREDICTIONS FOR RACES.

I CHECKED WITH THE BOOKIES ACROSS TOWN. THE MAN WHO PLACED THE LARGE BETS HADN'T SHOWN UP AGAIN. I EVENTUALLY MANAGED TO WORK OUT HOW FAR BACK THE SPATE OF BETTING ON COLLEGE RACES STARTED.

NOW I HAD TO TRY AND TRACK DOWN THOSE TWO POLICEMEN. I TOOK A CHANCE AND CALLED INSPECTOR SCOTT.

ANY PROGRESS ON THE NAYLOR MURDER, INSPECTOR?

NOTHING. I'M AFRAID IT'S JUST BEEN LEFT AS PRESUMED DEATH BY NATURAL CAUSES.

AND HOW DO YOU FEEL ABOUT THAT?

ERHM... NOT ENTIRELY SATISFIED.

OK. LET'S WALK A WHILE.

INSPECTOR SCOTT WAS TRYING HARD TO DO HIS JOB WELL, I COULD TELL THAT MUCH.

WHAT DO YOU KNOW ABOUT THESE TWO POLICE OFFICERS WHO TALKED TO TODD NAYLOR JUST BEFORE HIS DEATH?

I DID A LITTLE CHECKING OFF MY OWN BACK. I'M NOT SURE... THERE ARE TWO GUYS WHO WORK JUST OUT OF TOWN WHO FIT THE DESCRIPTION.

BUT LOOK, I'M NOT 100 PER CENT ON THIS AND YOU'VE GOT TO TREAD VERY CAREFULLY HERE.

I'LL NEED SOME NAMES AND PHOTOGRAPHS.

LISTEN, STONE, I CAN'T HELP YOU OFFICIALLY. IF ANYTHING GOES WRONG, YOU'RE ON YOUR OWN.

RIGHT... ON MY OWN.

IN THIS LIFE YOU'VE OFTEN JUST GO TO DO THE BEST YOU CAN IN DIFFICULT CIRCUMSTANCES... ALONE I HAD NO PROBLEM WITH THAT, BUT I ALSO KNEW HOW USEFUL IT WOUL BE TO HAVE BACK-UP.

YOU EARNED IT, BUT YOU AIN'T TAKIN' IT... CLEAR? LEAVE IT FOR THE RELATIVES.

DAH! OK, SARGE, YOU'RE RIGHT! I'M JUST GONNA HAVE TO RELY ON MY GOOD LOOKS TO MAKE MY FORTUNE!

WHAT'S GOING DOWN HERE, SARGE?

NOTHING, CAPTAIN. JUST A SMALL MISUNDERSTANDING.

OK. CARRY ON.

YOU GET TO KNOW HOW A MAN'S GOING TO REACT WHEN YOU SPEND TIME WITH THEM IN EXTREME SITUATIONS. I'D ALWAYS KNOWN THAT JOHN CARLTON WOULD NEVER BETRAY THE TRUST OF HIS ATHLETES AND THE UNIVERSITY. HE WAS A MAN OF RESPONSIBILTIES. NOW I OWED IT TO HIM TO TRACK DOWN WHO WAS BEHIND THE NAYLOR CASE. I WOULDN'T LEAVE HIM ON HIS OWN.

THANKS FOR COMING IN, JACQUELINE. HAVE A LOOK THROUGH THESE MUG SHOTS AND TELL IF YOU RECOGNIZE ANYONE.

JUST TAKE YOUR TIME. WE WANT YOU TO BE SURE.

OK... THESE TWO.. THEY'RE THE OFFICERS WHO TALKED TO TODD AND ME.

SURE?

COMPLETELY.

THANK YOU JACQUELINE. THAT HAS BEEN VERY HELPFUL.

I DECIDED TO CHECK OUT THESE TWO POLICE OFFICERS. WHILE I SPENT DAYS SITTING IN CARS OR STANDING ON STREET CORNERS, THE WORLD'S ATHLETES WERE REACTING TO BANNISTER'S SUB-FOUR-MINUTE MILE.

WES SANTEE STORMED TO A 4.01.3 MILE IN KANSAS CITY... A NEW U.S. RECORD. JOHN LANDY RAN HIS FIRST RACE IN FINLAND WITH AN AUSTRALIAN RECORD OF 4.01.6.

76

AT LAST IT WAS SUMMER. BANNISTER'S FOUR-MINUTE MILE WAS BARELY ONE-MONTH OLD.

I WAS PONDERING ANOTHER ANNIVERSARY... TEN YEARS SINCE D-DAY... WHEN WES SANTEE "THE KANSAS COWBOY", "THE DIZZY DEAN OF CINDERS", TOOK TO THE TRACK IN COMPTON, CALIFORNIA.

THE AMERICAN ATHLETIC UNION NEVER ALLOWED SANTEE THE BENEFIT OF PACEMAKERS.

QUICKLY HIS COMPETITORS FELL AWAY.

SANTEE HAD TO RUN ALONE FOR VIRTUALLY THE ENTIRE RACE.

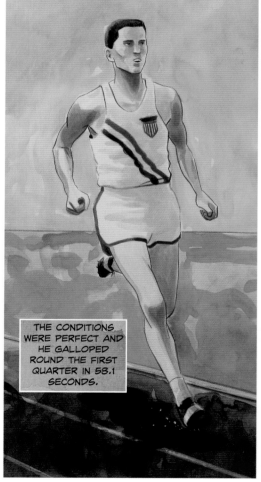

THE CONDITIONS WERE PERFECT AND HE GALLOPED ROUND THE FIRST QUARTER IN 58.1 SECONDS.

THE PISTOL WAS FIRED AS SANTEE PASSED THE 1500M MARK.

TRAILING THE TAPE FROM THE 1500M POINT, HE HURTLED TO THE MILE FINISH.

SLOWING EVER SO SLIGHTLY, HE JUST MISSED THE MAGIC BARRIER, FINISHING WITH 4.00.6 – THE SECOND FASTEST MILE IN HISTORY.

ALONG THE WAY, "THE KANSAS COWBOY" HAD RUN SO FAST THAT HE PASSED THE 1500M MARK IN A NEW WORLD RECORD.

WHATEVER HAPPENED NOW, WES SANTEE WOULD GO DOWN IN THE RECORD BOOKS AS A WORLD RECORD BREAKER.

THANKS FOR COMING TO ME WITH THIS INFORMATION.

WE HAD THOUGHT THAT THE DEATH THREATS AGAINST SANTEE WERE RELATED TO GAMBLING. WE'D BEEN INVESTIGATING SOME DIFFERENT ANGLES ON THIS.

SO WHAT HAPPENS NEXT, AGENT ASHENFELTER?

WE NAIL THIS CARTEL, FIND OUT WHO MURDERED TODD NAYLOR AND KEEP TRACK AND FIELD CLEAN.

LET'S GO FOR THE TWO SMALL GUYS FIRST, THEN WE'LL REEL IN THE CHIEF... LET'S SAVE HIM FOR THE LAST LAP, EH, STONE?

I FELT WE WERE APPROACHING THE BELL ON THIS CASE.

SANTEE WASTED NO TIME MAKING HIS NEXT ATTEMPT ON THE WORLD RECORD FOR THE MILE.

JUST ONE WEEK AFTER HIS VALIANT 4.00.6, HE RACED IN LOS ANGELES AGAINST JOSY BARTHEL, THE OLYMPIC 1500M CHAMPION.

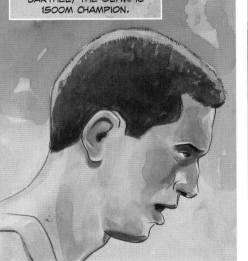

HE BIDED HIS TIME BEHIND BARTHEL, GOING THROUGH THE BELL AT 3.00.2.

DOWN THE BACK STRAIGHT HE STRUCK, STRIDING AWAY TO A GALLING 4.00.8... BUT HE HAD DESTROYED THE OLYMPIC CHAMPION.

WHERE DID HE THINK
HE COULD RUN TO?
IT WAS THE LAST RUN
OF A DESPERATE MAN!

BUT LACEY WASN'T
THAT QUICK. I CAUGHT
HIM BEFORE HE MADE
IT TO HIS CAR.

86

LEE AND LACEY WEREN'T SO TOUGH. THEY KNEW THEIR ONLY CHANCE WAS TO THROW AS MUCH OF THE BLAME AS POSSIBLE ONTO THE MAN WHO RAN THEM... CHIEF GREENWOOD.

AT FIRST, WE WERE JUST GETTING INSIDE INFORMATION FROM COACHING STAFF. IT WAS A BIT HIT AND MISS.

WE COLLECTED PROTECTION MONEY FOR THE BOSS FOR YEARS...THEN WE STARTED TO BET ON SPORTS.

...THEN WE STARTED TO BRIBE SOME COLLEGE ATHLETES TO THROW RACES OR IMPEDE OTHER ATHLETES IN RACES. ONLY A FEW DID IT...

...NAYLOR WAS A BIG NAME ON THE COLLEGE CIRCUIT. WE FELT IF HE COULD FINISH WHERE WE TOLD HIM TO WE COULD GET IN SOME BIG BETS BEFORE IT WAS TIME TO GET OUT...

...BUT HE WOULDN'T DO IT. THE BOSS WAS FURIOUS, SO HE SENT...

...BIG TONY OUT TO TALK TO HIM IN THE DESERT. AND HE MADE IT CLEAR THAT BIG TONY WAS TO...

...USE AS MUCH PERSUASION AS HE THOUGHT NECESSARY...

...BUT HE WASN'T HAPPY WHEN NAYLOR TURNED UP DEAD. SAID IT WAS TIME TO SWITCH SPORTS. BUT BIG TONY...

...HAD CROSSED SOME LINE. HE WAS HARDER TO DEAL WITH. HE MADE IT DIFFICULT FOR ALL OF US.

WELL, WE'VE GOT ENOUGH TO CONFRONT CHIEF GREENWOOD.

WHILE THE CASE WAS MOVING FORWARD, SO WAS THE WORLD RECORD FOR THE MILE.

RUNNING AT TURKU IN FINLAND ON 21 JUNE, JOHN LANDY TURNED THE WORLD OF MILE RUNNING ON ITS HEAD.

CHRIS CHATAWAY, WHO HAD PACED HIS FRIEND ROGER BANNISTER TO THE SUB-FOUR-MINUTE MILE, HAD GONE OVER TO FINLAND TO RACE LANDY.

SOME OF THE BRITISH PRESS THOUGHT CHATAWAY WAS UNPATRIOTIC PARTICIPATING IN A RACE TO HELP LANDY ATTACK BANNISTER'S RECORD.

BUT CHATAWAY SAID HE WAS JUST THERE TO RACE.

SO WAS JOHN LANDY.

CONDITIONS WERE CRISP AND CALM. THE BLACK CINDER TRACK WAS FAMOUS FOR FAST TIMES.

LANDY AND CHATAWAY QUICKLY PULLED AWAY FROM THE FIELD.

THAT NIGHT, LANDY HAD SOMETHING HE HADN'T HAD BEFORE... A RIVAL OTHER THAN THE CLOCK.

CHATAWAY WAS STILL THERE AS THEY CAME INTO THE LAST LAP. HE MADE HIS EFFORT ON THE FIRST BEND, BUT THE MAN FROM DOWN UNDER RESPONDED WITH DEVASTATING PACE.

EFFORTLESSLY BREAKING AWAY FROM CHATAWAY, LANDY SWEPT THROUGH 1500M, CLIPPING A SECOND OFF SANTEE'S WORLD RECORD.

BUT LANDY HAD EYES ONLY FOR THE FINAL PRIZE: THE WORLD RECORD FOR THE MILE.

3.41.8

HE RACED ACROSS THE LINE IN 3.57.9, SHATTERING BANNISTER'S TIME.

3.57.9

THE FOUR-MINUTE MILE HAD TAKEN SO LONG TO REACH AND NOW IT WAS SURPASSED WITH EASE!

JOHN LANDY AND ROGER BANNISTER WERE DUE TO MEET IN AUGUST AT THE BRITISH EMPIRE AND COMMONWEALTH GAMES IN CANADA.

THE TWO FASTEST MILERS IN HISTORY WOULD FIGHT IT OUT OVER THE MILE. THAT WOULD BE WORTH SEEING.

AMERICA WOULD NOT BE AT THE EMPIRE GAMES. "THE KANSAS COWBOY" WOULD HAVE TO COOL HIS SPURS AT HOME.

BY NOW INSPECTOR SCOTT AND AGENT ASHENFELTER BOTH HAD ADDITIONAL INCRIMINATING EVIDENCE AGAINST CHIEF GREENWOOD.

WHEN WE BARGED INTO HIS OFFICE, I COULD TELL THAT CHIEF GREENWOOD HAD BEEN WAITING FOR THIS DAY...

...I WOULD GUESS BY THE LOOK OF RESIGNATION ON HIS FACE HE'D BEEN WAITING FOR A LONG TIME.

I ALWAYS WONDERED WHAT I WOULD DO IF THIS DAY EVER CAME.

WHAT HAPPENED WITH TODD NAYLOR? DID YOU, LEE OR LACEY KILL HIM?

STRAIGHT TO THE POINT, HUH?

LET'S NOT WASTE ANY TIME HERE, SHALL WE? I'M AFRAID I DON'T HAVE ANY PATIENCE LEFT!

VERY WELL. NAYLOR WAS KILLED, BUT NOT BY THE THREE OF US. IT WAS AN ACCIDENT.

EXPLAIN.

WE HAD BEEN MAKING MODEST AMOUNTS OF MONEY BETTING ON SPORTS EVENTS. WE TRIED TO MAKE AS SURE OF THE OUTCOME AS WE COULD.

SOME EVENTS, LIKE HORSE RACING AND FIGHTS, ARE OFTEN FIXED BUT ARE ALSO HEAVILY SCRUTINIZED. WE CHOSE SPORTS WHICH NOBODY THOUGHT WOULD BE FIXED.

MORE BY CHANCE THAN DESIGN, WE HAD SOME SUCCESS, BUT RUNNERS WERE HARD TO CONTROL. TODD NAYLOR REFUSED TO GO ALONG WITH OUR PLANS. ONE MEMBER OF OUR GROUP WENT OUT TO CONFRONT HIM ONE EVENING.

THIS WAS "BIG TONY"?

YES. TONY ANDERSON.

WAIT! I REMEMBER HIM... HE WAS A POLICE OFFICER, RIGHT? GOT THROWN OFF THE FORCE FOR EMBEZZLEMENT.

YES. I THOUGHT HE MIGHT BE USEFUL TO US, BUT HE WAS TOO UNPREDICTABLE.

HE WENT TO SEE NAYLOR BY HIMSELF... HE THREATENED HIM... NAYLOR STEPPED BACK, LOST HIS FOOTING AND FELL. ON THE WAY DOWN HE CRACKED HIS HEAD AND AS A RESULT HE DIED. IT WAS AN ACCIDENT.

BUT NONE OF YOU REPORTED IT OR TRIED IN ANY WAY TO HELP HIM.

INSTEAD YOU COVERED YOUR TRACKS AND MOVED ALL THE INVESTIGATING OFFICERS OFF THE CASE ONTO ANOTHER.

YOU OBSTRUCTED THE DUE PROCESS OF THE LAW!

GREENWOOD HADN'T STARTED OUT AS A COP WITH THE INTENTION OF BEING CORRUPT, BUT HE'D GOTTEN GREEDY ALONG THE WAY. HE WASN'T STUPID. ALL ALONG A NAGGING VOICE KEPT TELLING HIM IT COULDN'T LAST... JUSTICE MUST BE SERVED!

AND IT WAS YOU WHO SENT BIG TONY OUT TO BEAT ON TODD NAYLOR.

YOU ARE A CHIEF OF POLICE! THE BUCK STOPS WITH YOU!

SO HE LEFT TODD FOR DEAD, COVERED HIS TRACKS AND IMPLICATED CARLTON WITH THAT ENVELOPE. THEN WHAT?

ANDERSON COULDN'T STOP AFTER THAT. HE BECAME OBSESSED WITH BETTING ON ATHLETICS.

HE STOLE COACH CARLTON'S BOOK ON THE FORM OF ATHLETES. LIKE CARLTON, HE BELIEVED WES SANTEE WOULD BREAK FOUR MINUTES FIRST AND PLACED ALL HIS MONEY ON HIM.

TODD NAYLOR WAS JUST THE WRONG GUY AT THE WRONG TIME. WHILE OTHERS HAD CHASED AFTER EASY MONEY, HE'D TOILED IN PURSUIT OF EXCELLENCE. AND WHAT HAD IT GOT HIM? AN ACCIDENTAL DEATH IN THE DESERT?

WE KNOW ABOUT HIS BETS... HE LOST BIG TIME.

SO WHERE IS HE NOW?

MISSING. WE CAN'T FIND HIM ANYWHERE.

YOU WERE A FOOL TO USE A LOOSE CANNON LIKE ANDERSON IN THE FIRST PLACE.

HE SHOULD NEVER HAVE EVEN BEEN A COP AT ALL! HIS WAR RECORD SHOWS HE WAS UNSTABLE AND UNTRUSTWORTHY. YOU JUST WANTED SOME MUSCLE ON YOUR SIDE!

I RECOGNIZE THAT NOW. HE WAS ALWAYS UNPREDICTABLE AND IN RETROSPECT SLIGHTLY UNHINGED. HE BLAMED SANTEE AND ROGER BANNISTER FOR EVERYTHING AND THREATENED TO KILL SANTEE.

THERE WAS MORE TO ANDERSON THAN YOU EVER REALIZED!

WHAT YOU DIDN'T KNOW AND WE'VE ONLY JUST FOUND OUT IS THAT ANDERSON WAS BEING BLACKMAILED BY COMMUNIST AGENTS. HE DIDN'T EVEN OWN HIS OWN LIFE! IN THE END, HE WAS WORKING FOR THEM AND YOU WERE BEING PLAYED!

ASHENFELTER HAD KEPT THAT ONE TO HIMSELF!

CHIEF GREENWOOD, THERE'LL BE AN OFFER ON THE TABLE FOR YOU, BUT LEE AND LACEY ARE FINISHED. YOU CO-OPERATE AND YOU STILL GET YOUR PENSION.

GREENWOOD DIDN'T LOOK LIKE HE WAS HAVING A GOOD DAY. I COULDN'T HAVE CARED LESS.

THIS DEPARTMENT GETS CLEANED UP!

SO THAT'S IT AT THE MOMENT, SIR. LEE AND LACEY ARE GOING DOWN, CHIEF GREENWOOD HAS "RETIRED" EARLY, BUT "BIG TONY" ANDERSON HAS GONE TO GROUND AND WE CAN'T BRING HIM IN YET.

I'VE BEEN TALKING TO MY CONTACTS AT THE FBI AND THE CIA. APPARENTLY TONY ANDERSON WAS BEING RUN BY A COMMUNIST CELL THAT WAS CHARGED WITH DISCREDITING WESTERN SPORTS. THEY DIDN'T WANT TO SEE A WESTERN ATHLETE BREAK FOUR MINUTES FOR THE MILE FIRST. IT WAS ANATHEMA TO THEIR CONCEPT OF SOVIET SUPERIORITY.

BUT THE UNIVERSITY IS PLEASED WITH YOUR WORK, DAN. THE DEAN IS VERY HAPPY THAT COACH CARLTON HAS COME OUT CLEAN AND THAT NO BLAME IS ATTACHED TO THE UNIVERSITY.

AND TODD NAYLOR'S ACTIONS REFLECTED WELL UPON THE UNIVERSITY. SEEMS HE WAS A YOUNG MAN WITH PRINCIPLES.

YES, WE'VE LOST ENOUGH OF THOSE OVER THE YEARS.

I JUST HOPE WE CAN BRING ANDERSON IN FOR THIS.

I KNOW YOU LIKE TO TIE UP ALL THE LOOSE ENDS, DAN, BUT ANDERSON IS SOMEONE ELSE'S PROBLEM. RIGHT NOW YOU'VE GOT SOME VACATION COMING. I GATHER YOU'RE OFF TO CANADA.

YES. I'M TAKING ALISON TO WATCH "THE MIRACLE MILE" IN VANCOUVER.

YOU LUCKY MAN. THEY'RE CALLING IT THE RACE OF THE CENTURY.

HAVE FUN.

I WILL. SEE YOU IN A WEEK.

RELAXED AS I WAS WHEN WE FLEW INTO VANCOUVER, I STILL FELT THAT I'D LEFT SOME UNFINISHED BUSINESS BEHIND ME.

STILL, TO SAY THAT I WAS EXCITED WOULD HAVE BEEN AN UNDERSTATEMENT.

I COULDN'T WAIT FOR THE LAST DAY OF COMPETITION AND "THE MIRACLE MILE", THE CLASH OF THE ONLY TWO SUB-FOUR-MINUTE MILERS IN THE WORLD.

WOW! IT'S SUCH A LOVELY DAY, DAN, BUT IT CERTAINLY IS HOT!

IS THAT GOOD FOR THE RUNNERS?

IT'S GREAT UNLESS YOU'RE ONE OF THOSE POOR SUCKERS RUNNING THE MARATHON.

26 MILES! I'M GLAD I'M NOT DOING IT!

DON'T FORGET THOSE EXTRA 385 YARDS!

HUH. I COULD SWEAR I JUST SAW... NO, IT COULDN'T BE. COME ON, LET'S GET INSIDE.

WE TRIED TO SURPRISE ANDERSON, BUT HE HEARD OUR FOOTSTEPS ON THE ROOFTOP.

WH... I KNOW YOU! GET BACK!

BANNISTER'S FIFTEEN YARDS DOWN, AT HALF WAY!

HE'LL NEVER GET THAT BACK.

PUT THE GUN DOWN, MAN.

TODD NAYLOR'S DEATH MAY HAVE BEEN AN ACCIDENT, BUT THIS... THIS WILL BE COLD-BLOODED MURDER!

I LOOKED INTO HIS EYES AND I KNEW THAT STARE. I'D SEEN IT ON MANY MEN DURING THE WAR.

THERE WAS NO GOING BACK FOR ANDERSON NOW.

104

WILLYA LOOK AT THAT!

FERGUSON GOT THE BRONZE FOR CANADA!

WE'LL NEVER SEE A RACE LIKE THAT AGAIN!

JUST STAY STILL NOW. YOU'RE NOT GOING ANYWHERE.

FOR THE FIRST TIME IN ONE RACE TWO RUNNERS HAD BROKEN FOUR MINUTES.

ROGER BANNISTER HAD HAD TO RUN HIS QUICKEST EVER MILE TO BEAT THE GALLANT JOHN LANDY... IT WAS MAGNIFICENT. THIS REALLY WAS "THE MILE OF THE CENTURY"!

WHEN THE RACE WAS DONE, THERE STILL STOOD TWO GREAT SPORTSMEN... GENTLEMEN TO THE END.

WELL DONE, SIR. WE'LL TAKE IT FROM HERE. THIS MAN IS GOING STRAIGHT INTO CUSTODY.

IF YOU EVER WANT A JOB IN VANCOUVER, GIVE US A CALL.

THANKS. I MIGHT JUST DO THAT ONE DAY.

BANNISTER ACKNOWLEDGED THE APPLAUSE OF THE CROWD AND I MADE MY WAY BACK TO ALISON.

DAN! DID YOU SEE THE RACE?

I CAUGHT ALL THE KEY MOMENTS. I'M GLAD I SAW THAT FINISH.

IT WAS JUST ABSOLUTELY SENSATIONAL. NOW I KNOW WHY YOU LOVE THIS SPORT.

OH MY GOD!

WHAT?

LOOK!

I WILL NEVER FORGET THE SIGHT OF JIM PETERS STRUGGLING AROUND THE STADIUM.

HE WAS THE WORLD'S GREATEST MARATHON RUNNER. HE'D BROKEN THE WORLD RECORD FOUR TIMES.

TODAY HE HAD A LEAD OF THREE MILES WHEN HE CAME INTO THE STADIUM, BUT IT WAS A FEROCIOUSLY HOT DAY... 86 IN THE SHADE.

PETERS HADN'T TAKEN A DRINK OF WATER DURING THE RACE.

AT FIRST I THOUGHT MAYBE THERE WAS ANOTHER SNIPER. MAYBE HE'D BEEN SHOT. BUT THERE WAS NO BLOOD... ONLY SWEAT!

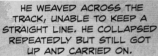

HE WEAVED ACROSS THE TRACK, UNABLE TO KEEP A STRAIGHT LINE. HE COLLAPSED REPEATEDLY BUT STILL GOT UP AND CARRIED ON.

THIS HARROWING SIGHT WAS AS GRIPPING AS A PRIZE FIGHT KNOCK DOWN.

ALL WE WANTED WAS TO RUN ONTO THE TRACK AND CARRY HIM TO THE FINISH.

PETERS EVENTUALLY MADE IT TO THE FINISH LINE... OR SO HE THOUGHT.

IN A CRUEL TWIST OF FATE, NEITHER PETERS NOR HIS TEAM MANAGERS KNEW THAT THE FINISH TO THE MARATHON HAD BEEN MOVED PAST THE NORMAL FINISH A FURTHER 200 YARDS.

THIS VALIANT MAN CAME AWAY WITH NOTHING.

BUT HIS EFFORTS WERE HEROIC AND INSPIRING.

Notes

Sydney Wooderson, "The Mighty Atom", won gold in the European championships at 1500m in 1938 and at 5000m in 1946 (in third place in that race was a young Emil Zatopek). He was undoubtedly at his peak during World War Two but was obviously unable to compete at any Olympics during those years. He was the last British man before Sebastian Coe to hold the world records for 800m, 1500m and the mile at the same time. At 5ft 6in, suffering from poor eyesight and bouts of rheumatic fever, he is best remembered for running the fastest mile of his life when he came second to the Swede Arne Andersson in August 1945 at White City in London. A young Roger Bannister was in the crowd and from that day Wooderson became his hero.

Roger Bannister had come fourth in the 1500m final at the 1952 Helsinki Olympics. His failure to win a medal in those Olympics spurred him on to the sub-four-minute mile in 1954. After winning the mile in Vancouver, he went to the European championships in Bern, where 22 days later he won the 1500m final. After that, he retired from the sport to concentrate on his career as a doctor in the field of neurology. He was knighted in 1975.

John Landy went on to run more sub-four-minute miles. In 1956, he won a bronze medal in the Melbourne Olympic 1500m final. He qualified for the Australian team by winning the national championships despite stopping to see if youngster Ron Clarke was all right after a fall. A gentleman throughout his career, he went on to become governor of the state of Victoria in Australia.

Wes Santee had competed in the 5000m at the Helsinki Olympics. During his career, he set world records for 1500m both outdoors and indoors, as well as an indoor world record for the mile. In 1955, he came second in the Pan American games championships over 1500m. The following year, he was banned from the sport by the Amateur Athletic Union in America for accepting expenses for appearing at three track meets where he helped fill the stands.

Bannister's two pacemakers went on to race themselves into history as well. Chris Chataway, who had finished fifth in the 1952 Olympic 5000m final after falling on the last bend, went on to run a world record in that event in 1954, as well as pick up a silver medal at the European Championships. He also ran his own sub-four-minute mile. After athletics, he went on to become a member of parliament in Britain. Chris Brasher, the other pacemaker, was regarded as the least talented of the group yet he achieved what none of the others did: an Olympic gold medal in the steeplechase at the 1956 Olympics. He had a more profound effect on British athletics than even Bannister, as he went on to co-found the London Marathon. Today the London Marathon donates large sums of money each year to support the development of British endurance runners.

Emil Zatopek, "The Czech Locomotive", won gold and silver at the 1948 Olympics and went on to achieve an outstanding treble of golds in the 1952 Olympics when he won the 5000m, the 10,000m and the marathon (the decision to take part in the marathon was a last-minute one. He had never run the event before). Zatopek revolutionized running and training. He developed intense interval workouts that changed how athletes trained forever. In 1968, Zatopek, an outspoken supporter of "The Prague Spring", was stripped of his rank of Colonel in the Czech army and forced to work in a number of menial jobs, including as a dustbin man. After the Iron Curtain came down, his life improved and in 1998 Emil was awarded the Order of the White Lion, a national honour presented to him by Czech President Vaclav Havel. He died in 2000 of pneumonia.